The approved documents

What is an approved document?

The Secretary of State has approved a series of documents that give practical guidance about how to meet the requirements of the Building Regulations 2010 for England. Approved documents give guidance on each of the technical parts of the regulations and on regulation 7 (see the back of this document).

Approved documents set out what, in ordinary circumstances, may be accepted as reasonable provision for compliance with the relevant requirements of the Building Regulations to which they refer. If you follow the guidance in an approved document, there will be a presumption of compliance with the requirements covered by the guidance. However, compliance is not guaranteed; for example, 'normal' guidance may not apply if the particular case is unusual in some way.

Note that there may be other ways to comply with the requirements – *there is no obligation to adopt any particular solution contained in an approved document*. If you prefer to meet a relevant requirement in some other way than described in an approved document, you should discuss this with the relevant building control body.

In addition to guidance, some approved documents include provisions that must be followed exactly, as required by regulations or where methods of test or calculation have been prescribed by the Secretary of State.

Each approved document relates only to the particular requirements of the Building Regulations that the document addresses. However, building work must also comply with any other applicable requirements of the Building Regulations.

How to use this approved document

This document uses the following conventions.

a. Text against a green background is an extract from the Building Regulations 2010 or the Building (Approved Inspectors etc.) Regulations 2010 (both as amended). These extracts set out the legal requirements of the regulations.

b. Key terms, printed in green, are defined in Appendix A.

c. When this approved document refers to a named standard or other document, the relevant version is listed in Appendix B. However, if the issuing body has revised or updated the listed version of the standard or document, you may use the new version as guidance if it continues to address the relevant requirements of the Building Regulations.

NOTE: Standards and technical approvals may also address aspects of performance or matters that are not covered by the Building Regulations, or they may recommend higher standards than required by the Building Regulations.

Where you can get further help

If you do not understand the technical guidance or other information in this approved document or the additional detailed technical references to which it directs you, you can seek further help through a number of routes, some of which are listed below.

a. The Planning Portal website: www.planningportal.gov.uk.

b. *If you are the person undertaking the building work:* either from your local authority building control service or from an approved inspector.

c. *If you are registered with a competent person scheme:* from the scheme operator.

d. *If your query is highly technical:* from a specialist or an industry technical body for the relevant subject.

The Building Regulations

The following is a high level summary of the Building Regulations relevant to most types of building work. Where there is any doubt you should consult the full text of the regulations, available at www.legislation.gov.uk.

Building work

Regulation 3 of the Building Regulations defines 'building work'. Building work includes:

a. the erection or extension of a building

b. the provision or extension of a controlled service or fitting

c. the material alteration of a building or a controlled service or fitting.

Regulation 4 states that building work should be carried out in such a way that, when work is complete:

a. for new buildings or work on a building that complied with the applicable requirements of the Building Regulations: the building complies with the applicable requirements of the Building Regulations.

b. for work on an existing building that did not comply with the applicable requirements of the Building Regulations:

   (i) the work itself must comply with the applicable requirements of the Building Regulations

   (ii) the building must be no more unsatisfactory in relation to the requirements than before the work was carried out.

Material change of use

Regulation 5 defines a 'material change of use' in which a building or part of a building that was previously used for one purpose will be used for another.

The Building Regulations set out requirements that must be met before a building can be used for a new purpose. To meet the requirements, the building may need to be upgraded in some way.

Energy efficiency requirements

Part 6 of the Building Regulations imposes additional specific requirements for energy efficiency.

If a building is extended or renovated, the energy efficiency of the existing building or part of it may need to be upgraded.

Notification of work

Most building work and material changes of use must be notified to a building control body unless one of the following applies.

a. It is work that will be self-certified by a registered competent person or certified by a registered third party.

b. It is work exempted from the need to notify by regulation 12(6A) of, or Schedule 4 to, the Building Regulations.

Responsibility for compliance

People who are responsible for building work (e.g. agent, designer, builder or installer) must ensure that the work complies with all applicable requirements of the Building Regulations. The building owner may also be responsible for ensuring that work complies with the Building Regulations. If building work does not comply with the Building Regulations, the building owner may be served with an enforcement notice.

Contents

The approved documents Page i

The Building Regulations iii

Approved Document 7: Materials and workmanship **1**

Summary 1

Continuing control 1

Interaction with other legislation 1

Regulation 7 of the Building Regulations **2**

Performance and limitations **3**

Performance 3

Limitations 3

Section 1: Materials **4**

Ways of establishing the fitness of materials 4

Short-lived materials 6

Materials susceptible to changes in their properties 6

Section 2: Workmanship **7**

Ways of establishing the adequacy of workmanship 7

Appendix A: Key terms **9**

Appendix B: Standards referred to **10**

Appendix C: Documents referred to **11**

Approved Document 7: Materials and workmanship

Summary

0.1 This approved document gives guidance on how to comply with regulation 7 of the Building Regulations. It contains the following sections:

Section 1: Materials
Section 2: Workmanship.

Continuing control

0.2 There are no provisions under the Building Regulations for continuing control over the materials used in building work following completion of the work. However, under section 19 of the Building Act 1984, local authorities may impose conditions with regard to the proposed use of prescribed short-lived materials, even when the plans conform to the regulations. However, no materials are currently prescribed for the purpose of section 19.

Interaction with other legislation

0.3 The Construction Products Regulation requires that construction products that are covered by a harmonised European product standard or conform to a European Technical Assessment should normally have CE marking.

Regulation 7 of the Building Regulations

This approved document gives guidance on how to meet regulation 7 of the Building Regulations 2010.

Regulation

Materials and workmanship

7. Building work shall be carried out—

(a) with adequate and proper materials which—

(i) are appropriate for the circumstances in which they are used,

(ii) are adequately mixed or prepared, and

(iii) are applied, used or fixed so as adequately to perform the functions for which they are designed; and

(b) in a workmanlike manner.

Performance and limitations

Performance

In the Secretary of State's view, you will meet the requirements of regulation 7 if you satisfy both of the following conditions.

a. Materials are of a suitable nature and quality in relation to the purposes and conditions of their use.

b. Workmanship is such that, where relevant, materials are adequately mixed or prepared and applied, used or fixed so as to perform adequately the functions for which they are intended.

Materials include:

a. manufactured products such as components, fittings, items of equipment and systems

b. naturally occurring materials such as stone, timber and thatch

c. backfilling for excavations in connection with building work.

Limitations

Regulation 7 applies to all building work. However, in accordance with regulation 8 and Schedule 1, the standards of materials and workmanship need be no more than are necessary to:

a. *for Parts A–D, F–K, N and P (except for paragraphs G2, H2 and J7) of Schedule 1:* secure reasonable standards of health or safety for people in or about the building

b. *for Part E of Schedule 1:* secure reasonable resistance to the passage of sound for the welfare and convenience of people in or about the building

c. *for Part L of Schedule 1:* conserve fuel and power

d. *for Part M of Schedule 1:* provide access to buildings and their facilities for people.

Section 1: Materials

1.1 Building work must meet the functional requirements of Schedule 1 to the Building Regulations. Approved documents refer to materials covered by harmonised European product standards, British Standards and other technical specifications. However, there is no obligation to adopt any particular solution contained in an approved document in order to meet functional requirements; the references are not exclusive and other materials may be suitable in the particular circumstances.

Ways of establishing the fitness of materials

1.2 You can assess the suitability of a material for use for a specific purpose in a number of ways, as described in paragraphs 1.3 to 1.21.

CE marking under the Construction Products Regulation

1.3 Many materials are construction products that have CE marking under the Construction Products Regulation (305/2011/EU-CPR).

The Construction Products Regulation requires that construction products on the EU market covered by a harmonised European product standard should normally have CE marking. In addition, manufacturers of products not covered by a harmonised standard can choose to affix CE marking to their products by obtaining a European Technical Assessment.

NOTE: You can find a list of the harmonised product standards under the Construction Products Regulation on the NANDO information system website at http://ec.europa.eu/enterprise/newapproach/nando/index.cfm?fuseaction=cpd.hs.

1.4 CE marking includes the reference of the product standard and the levels or classes of performance being declared against some or all of the characteristics covered by the standard. The CE marking should be on the product, its label, the packaging or accompanying documents. The CE symbol by itself does not necessarily indicate that the material is suitable for the building work.

1.5 In addition to CE marking, the product will have a declaration of performance containing more detailed information on the product. This may be a paper or electronic document, or it may be on a website.

It is essential to check that the declared performance is suitable for the building works.

1.6 In the absence of indications to the contrary, the building control body should assume that the information given in the CE marking and declaration of performance is accurate and reliable, and that the product meets the declared performance.

1.7 If the declared performance of a product is suitable for its intended use, the building control body should not prohibit or impede the use of the product.

CE marking under other EU directives and regulations

1.8 Products may have CE marking under European legislation such as the Gas Appliances Directive or the Pressure Equipment Directive. Such CE marking shows that the product meets the essential requirements set out in the legislation – for example, minimum safety requirements – and can be placed on the EU market.

1.9 Some products have CE marking in accordance with both the Construction Products Regulation and other legislation. The CE marking shows that the product complies with the requirements in all relevant EU legislation.

British Standards

1.10 Nearly all British Standards for construction products are the British versions of harmonised European standards used for CE marking. The BSI numbering policy is to adopt the CEN numbering, prefaced with BS, e.g. **BS EN 197-1:2000**.

1.11 Some British Standards are the British version of non-harmonised European standards; these also adopt the CEN numbering, prefaced with BS. These do not contain an Annex ZA, so CE marking cannot be affixed to products made to these standards.

1.12 Some British Standards for products not covered by a European standard will continue to exist.

1.13 Where a construction product has been made and assessed in accordance with one or more British Standards referred to in 1.11 and 1.12, this may show whether the product is suitable for its intended use.

Other national and international technical specifications

1.14 An international technical specification, including those prepared by ISO, or a national technical specification of a country other than the UK, may be used to demonstrate that a product not covered by a harmonised European standard meets the performance requirements of the Building Regulations.

Where necessary, the person who intends to carry out the work should obtain translations of specifications and demonstrate how the material meets the requirements of regulation 7.

NOTE: The national technical specifications of EU member states (and non-EU countries that are full members of CEN) are being progressively replaced by harmonised European standards, as is the case with British Standards.

Independent certification schemes

1.15 There are many independent product certification schemes in the UK and elsewhere that may provide information on the performance of a product. Such schemes certify that a material complies with the requirements of a recognised document and indicates it is suitable for its intended purpose and use. These may be in addition to, but not conflict with, CE marking.

NOTE: Materials which are not certified by an independent scheme might still conform to a relevant standard.

1.16 Accreditation of a certification body by a national accreditation body belonging to the European co-operation for Accreditation (EA) provides a means of demonstrating that their certification scheme can be relied upon. In the UK, most independent certification bodies are accredited by the United Kingdom Accreditation Service (UKAS), which belongs to the EA.

It is important to check the scope of the accreditation of a certification body, as accreditation might cover only part of the certification body's testing or certification business.

Tests and calculations

1.17 Where there is no relevant harmonised European standard, tests, calculations or other means may be used to demonstrate that the material can perform the function for which it is intended. UKAS or an equivalent national accreditation body belonging to the EA may accredit the testing laboratories; this accreditation provides a means of showing that tests can be relied on.

Past experience

1.18 Past experience, such as use in an existing building, may show that the material can perform the function for which it is intended.

Sampling

1.19 Under regulation 46 of the Building Regulations, local authorities have the power to take samples as necessary to establish whether materials to be used in building work comply with the provisions of the regulations.

1.20 Regulation 46 does not apply to any work specified in an initial notice or to any work for which a final certificate has been given by an approved inspector and accepted by the local authority.

1.21 Regulation 8 of the Building (Approved Inspectors etc.) Regulations 2010 provides that an approved inspector, having given an initial notice which continues to be in force, may take samples of material as are reasonable to establish within the limits of professional skill and care that regulation 7 of the Building Regulations or any other applicable regulations are complied with.

Short-lived materials

1.22 Some materials, in the absence of special care, may be considered unsuitable because of their rapid deterioration in relation to the expected life of the building.

1.23 A short-lived material which is readily accessible for inspection, maintenance and replacement may meet the requirements of the regulations if the consequences of failure are not likely to be serious to the health or safety of people in and around the building.

1.24 If a short-lived material is not readily accessible for inspection, maintenance and replacement, and the consequences of failure are likely to be serious for health or safety, it is unlikely that the material will meet the requirements of the regulations.

1.25 As noted in paragraph 0.2, local authorities have the power to impose conditions on the use of short-lived materials.

Materials susceptible to changes in their properties

1.26 The properties of some materials can change in certain environmental conditions. These changes can affect the performance of the materials over time.

1.27 Materials that are susceptible to changes in their properties may be used in building work and will meet the requirements of the regulations if the residual properties, including the structural properties, meet both of the following conditions.

a. Residual properties can be estimated at the time of their incorporation in the work.

b. Residual properties are shown to be adequate for the building to perform the function for which it is intended, for the expected life of the building.

Section 2: Workmanship

Ways of establishing the adequacy of workmanship

2.1 Examples of ways to establish the adequacy of workmanship are described in paragraphs 2.2 to 2.11.

CE marking

2.2 If a material has CE marking, workmanship may be specified in the relevant European Technical Assessment or harmonised product standard.

Standards

2.3 Methods of carrying out different types of work are also given in British Standards or other appropriate technical specifications.

NOTE: The **BS 8000** series of standards on workmanship on building sites combines guidance from other BSI codes and standards. The various parts of **BS 8000** are listed in appendix B.

Independent certification schemes

2.4 Some independent certification schemes specify how workmanship will deliver a declared level of performance. The person carrying out the work should show that the workmanship will provide the appropriate level of protection and performance.

2.5 Schemes, including competent person self-certification schemes, that register installers of materials can provide a means of ensuring that work has been carried out by knowledgeable contractors to appropriate standards.

Management systems

2.6 The quality of workmanship is covered by a quality management scheme, such as one that complies with the relevant recommendations of **BS EN ISO 9000** and related series of standards. There are a number of such UKAS-accredited schemes.

Past experience

2.7 Past experience, such as use in an existing building, may show that workmanship is appropriate for the function for which it is intended.

Tests

2.8 Tests can be used to show that workmanship is appropriate.

2.9 In the following three instances, the Building Regulations require those carrying out building work to have testing carried out to demonstrate compliance.

a. Sound insulation as described in regulation 41.

b. Air flow rate of mechanical ventilation as described in regulation 42.

c. Pressure testing as described in regulation 43.

2.10 Under regulation 45 of the Building Regulations 2010, regulation 8 of the Building (Approved Inspectors etc.) Regulations 2010 and section 33 of the Building Act 1984, building control bodies have powers to make tests as they consider necessary to establish whether building work complies with the requirements of regulation 7.

2.11 Those carrying out building work may voluntarily include testing in the activities they carry out to demonstrate that the work complies with the requirements of the regulations.

Appendix A: Key terms

The following are key terms used in this document:

BSI
The British Standards Institution is the UK national standards body. BSI publishes European standards in the UK as BS EN. Further information is available at: www.bsigroup.co.uk

Building control body
A local authority or an approved inspector.

CEN
The Comité Européen de Normalisation is the European standards body that prepares harmonised European product standards. Declarations of performance against such standards should provide sufficient information for any member state to allow the product onto its market and for specifiers and users to be able to assess whether the product is suitable for its intended use.

CEN also prepares non-harmonised European standards, such as test or calculation standards and standards for products or services that have not been mandated under a CE Marking Directive.

CEN does not issue standards directly, only through national standards bodies; BSI is the designated standards body for the UK.

Further information is available at: www.cen.eu

EA
The European co-operation for Accreditation is the umbrella organisation for all national accreditation bodies in Europe. Product certification bodies, inspection bodies and test laboratories approved by national accreditation bodies belonging to EA are equivalent to those approved by UKAS. Further information is available at: www.european-accreditation.org

European Technical Assessments
A favourable technical assessment issued under the European Construction Products Regulation 2011 that allows a manufacturer to affix CE markings on their products. Further information is available at: www.eota.eu

ISO
The International Organization for Standardization is the worldwide federation of national standards institutions. Standards are identified by 'ISO' and a number. ISO standards may be published separately or transposed into the UK as BS ISO or BS EN ISO. Further information is available at: www.iso.org

Materials
Materials include manufactured products such as components, fittings, items of equipment and systems; naturally occurring materials such as stone, timber and thatch; and backfilling for excavations in connection with building work.

NANDO
New Approach Notified and Designated Organisations is an information system produced by the European Commission. It lists the harmonised European standards and the bodies notified by member states to carry out conformity assessment tasks for CE marking. Further information is available at: http://ec.europa.eu/enterprise/newapproach/nando

UKAS
The United Kingdom Accreditation Service is the sole national accreditation body recognised by the UK government to assess, against internationally agreed standards, organisations that provide certification, testing, inspection and calibration services. Accreditation by UKAS demonstrates the competence, impartiality and performance capability of these organisations. Further information is available at: www.ukas.com

Appendix B: Standards referred to

BS EN ISO 9000
Quality management systems. Fundamentals and vocabulary [2005]

BS EN ISO 9001
Quality management systems. Requirements [2008]

BS 8000-1
Workmanship on building sites. Code of practice for excavation and filling [1989]

BS 8000-2-1
Workmanship on building sites. Code of practice for concrete work. Mixing and transporting concrete [1990 + AMD 9324].

BS 8000-2-2
Workmanship on building sites. Code of practice for concrete work. Sitework with in situ and precast concrete [1990]

BS 8000-3
Workmanship on building sites. Code of practice for masonry [2001]

BS 8000-4
Workmanship on building sites. Code of practice for waterproofing [1989]

BS 8000-5
Workmanship on building sites. Code of practice for carpentry, joinery and general fixings [1990]

BS 8000-6
Workmanship on building sites. Code of practice for slating and tiling of roofs and claddings [1990]

BS 8000-7
Workmanship on building sites. Code of practice for glazing [1990]

BS 8000-8
Workmanship on building sites. Code of practice for plasterboard partitions and dry linings [1994]

BS 8000-9
Workmanship on building sites. Cementitious levelling screeds and wearing screeds. Code of practice [2003]

BS 8000-11
Workmanship on building sites. Internal and external wall and floor tiling. Ceramic and agglomerated stone tiles, natural stone and terrazzo tiles and slabs, and mosaics. Code of practice [2011]

BS 8000-12
Workmanship on building sites. Code of practice for decorative wallcoverings and painting [1989]

BS 8000-13
Workmanship on building sites. Code of practice for above ground drainage and sanitary appliances [1989]

BS 8000-14
Workmanship on building sites. Code of practice for below ground drainage [1989]

BS 8000-15
Workmanship on building sites. Code of practice for hot and cold water services (domestic scale) [1990]

BS 8000-16
Workmanship on building sites. Code of practice for sealing joints in buildings using sealants [1997 + A1:2010]

Appendix C: Documents referred to

Legislation

Building Act 1984 c.55 (as amended)

Building Regulations 2010 (SI 2010/2214) (as amended)

Building (Approved Inspectors etc.) Regulations 2010 (SI 2010/2215) (as amended)

Construction Products Regulation (305/2011/EU-CPR)

Gas Appliances Directive (2009/142/EC)

Pressure Equipment Directive (97/23/EC)

The Welsh Ministers (Transfer of Functions) (No. 2) Order 2009 (SI 2009/3019)